AGE 7-10

MY QURAN WORKBOOK

PUZZLES
CROSSWORDS
WORDSEARCHES
COLORING
AND MANY OTHER ACTIVITIES

by
TAHERA KASSAMALI

Goodword**kidz**

Helping you build a family of faith

Goodword Books
1, Nizamuddin West Market, New Delhi - 110 013
email:info@goodwordbooks.com
first published by Goodword Books in 2004
in arrangement with Tayyiba Publishers & Distributors
Reprinted 2007(twice), 2008
Printed in India
© Goodword Books 2008

www.goodwordbooks.com

MY QURAN WORKBOOK

Children need to learn Islamic teachings in a way which takes into consideration the mind of a child. Learning about religion is sometimes taken as serious and even boring. In order to change that negative conception, educators and parents need to use more appealing methods to put the message of Islam across to the younger generation. This book has been designed with that purpose in mind, and we hope that both parents and educators will enjoy going through it.

For the parent

Our experience shows that no book or teacher can take the place of a parent when it comes to teaching children religious beliefs and practices. We urge that parents use this book as a tool in their efforts to help their children understand and appreciate Islam. The following points are suggested.

1. The activities in this book cater for children around the ages of 7-10. Some of these children may require a little help with some activities. Work together with your child through these pages to encourage an enthusiasm for learning and thinking about Islamic teachings. Rather than providing all the answers, help him/her to think and answer.

2. Please provide your child with a good translation of the Holy Qur'an. Read the ayaat and the meanings with your child to help him/her complete the activities. This could be very useful in initiating an interest in the contents of the Qur'an. Continue to encourage recitation with meaning even after the workbook is completed.

3. This workbook would be very useful for the children's programs which take place in many communities during Ramadhan. We request that parents and teachers buy these books from us rather than photocopying pages, so that future production of such books continues to be possible. Please contact us regarding discounts for bulk copies.

Please continue to encourage your child to learn more about Islam. To instill an appreciation for religious beliefs and practices in a young mind is the most rewarding thing you can do for your child. The effects could last a lifetime.

Rajab 1418
November 1997

اَفَلاَ يَتَدَبَّرُوْنَ الْقُرْآنَ
اَمْ عَلٰى قُلُوْبٍ اَقْفَالُهَا

Why do they not ponder
over the Qur'an, or are
there locks on the hearts?

(47:24)

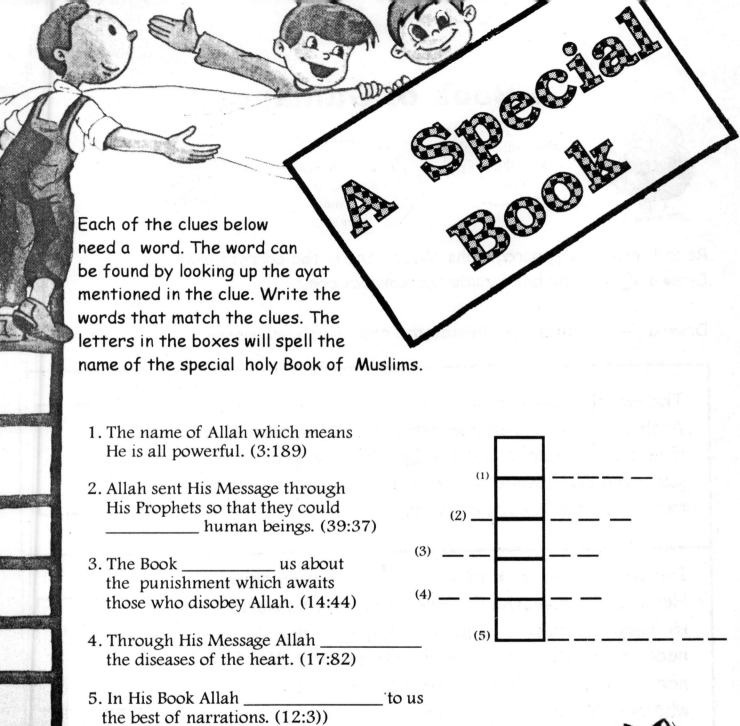

A Special Book

Each of the clues below need a word. The word can be found by looking up the ayat mentioned in the clue. Write the words that match the clues. The letters in the boxes will spell the name of the special holy Book of Muslims.

1. The name of Allah which means He is all powerful. (3:189)

2. Allah sent His Message through His Prophets so that they could _____ human beings. (39:37)

3. The Book _____ us about the punishment which awaits those who disobey Allah. (14:44)

4. Through His Message Allah _____ the diseases of the heart. (17:82)

5. In His Book Allah _____ to us the best of narrations. (12:3))

(1) ☐ _ _ _ _ _
(2) _ ☐ _ _ _ _
(3) _ _ ☐ _ _ _
(4) _ _ ☐ _ _ _
(5) ☐ _ _ _ _ _ _

5

A Book of Guidance

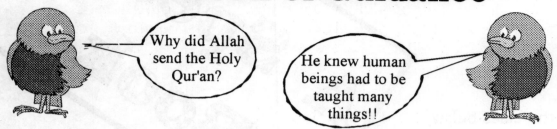

Read the following paragraphs. Which one is the correct one?
Draw a 🙂 in the box beside the correct one.

Draw a 🙁 in the boxes beside the ones which are wrong.

The Holy Qur an is a book from Allah. It is written in Arabic. There is great reward to read the book. Even if we do not understand the Qur'an, it is enough to just read and respect it. Only the Scholars of Islam need to understand the Qur'an.	
In the Holy Qur'an Allah talks to the human beings. He guides and teaches us how to live in this world. He shows us what is right and what is wrong. We need to read the Qur'an and understand it. We need to follow the rules of the Qur'an. That is what the Qur'an was sent for.	
The Holy Qur'an was sent by Allah so Muslims would have a holy book to show the non-Muslims. Since not all the Muslims know and understand Arabic it is all right for them to just respect the Qur'an and keep it in a safe place. They can make a beautiful cover for it and put it away.	

The Books of Allah

The Prophets of Allah received Revelation from Allah.
This was then written down in a book to guide people.
Some of these books are written below.
Do you know who they were given to?
Write the name of the Prophet beside each book.

Suhuf	given to Prophet _____
Zabur	given to Prophet _____
Tawrat	given to Prophet _____
Injeel	given to Prophet _____

Names of the Holy Qur'an

The Qur'an has many names.
Ahmad's teacher has written four names of the Qur'an.
She has also written the meanings of the names.
But the meanings are not in correct order.
Help Ahmad join each name to its correct meaning.

Name	Meaning
Huda	Distinction
Furqan	Narration
Dhikr	Guidance
Bayan	Rememberance

8

Titles of the Qur'an

The Holy Qur'an uses different words to describe itself. These are its titles. Many of these titles can be seen on the cover of the Holy Qur'an. Do you know what is the title on your copy of the Qur'an? Below are some titles of the Qur'an. Under them are the meanings of the titles. Color each title and its meaning in the same color.

Al-Qur'an al-Karim

Al-Qur'an al-Hakim

Al-Qur'an al-Majid

The Glorious Qur'an

The Noble Qur'an

The Wise Qur'an

The Final Word of Allah

The first box below explains the belief of Muslims that the Qur'an is the last book sent by Allah. The second box has many mistakes. Read both boxes and then underline what is wrong in box two.

The Last Message

The Holy Qur'an is the last of the Holy Books sent by Allah. It was given to the last Prophet, Muhammad (s) and will remain the holy book until the day of Judgement. Allah himself has said He will protect it, and not even one ayat of it will change. The Qur'an that Muslims have today has exactly the same Ayaat which were revealed to the Prophet in Makkah.

The Last Message

The Holy Qur'an is the message of Allah given to the Prophet Ibrahim (a). It was revealed in Makkah. Because there have been many changes made by human beings in the Qur'an, Muslims are now waiting for another Prophet to bring the last message. Parts of the Qur'an have been lost and no-one knows where they are. Muslims hope to take better care of the next message from Allah.

10

Draw a Qur'an

Look at the picture of the Qur'an. Now try to draw a similar Qur'an. Make sure you include details such as the Qur'an stand and the Qur'an bookmark. Then color your picture.

Names of Surahs

After the ayaat of Quran were divided into surahs, each surah was given a name. This makes it easier to refer to a particular surah. How many names of surahs do you know? Find out the names of the surahs below.

A surah named after the person who built the Ka'bah with his son.

If you know the Prophet who was swallowed by a whale, you know this sura.

The surah that gets its name because of its being the first in the Qur'an.

A surah named after something you use for writing.

This surah is named after the trip to Makkah made by Muslims in the month of Dhul Hijjah.

The Qur'an tells many stories. This surah is the Arabic word for stories.

The Law of Qur'an Recitation

The recitation of Qur'an is known as Tilawah. Tilawah should be done in a special way. There are many rules of Tilawah. These rules are there in the Qur'an itself. Below are three ayaat of Qur'an which give us some laws of Tilawah. Read each ayat and then complete the sentence beside it.

Law

لَا يَمَسُّهُ اِلَّا الْمُطَهَّرُوْنَ

Before I recite the Qur'an I must do

_____

Law

None can touch it (the Qur'an) except the purified ones.

56:79

Law

فَاِذَا قَرَأْتَ الْقُرْآنَ فَاسْتَعِذْ بِاللّهِ مِنَ الشَّيْطٰنِ الرَّجِيْمِ

Before I recite the Qur'an I must seek help against

_____

Law

And when you recite the Qur'an seek refuge in Allah from the accursed Shaytan

16:98

Law

لَا تُحَرِّكْ بِهِ لِسَانَكَ لِتَعْجَلَ بِهِ

When I am reciting the Qur'an I must not

_____

Law

Do not move your tongue with it (the Qur'an) to make haste.

75:16

An Easy Crossword

Across

2. The month in which the Qur'an was revealed.
4. The Prophet (s) received the first revelation in the cave of this mountain.
6. The angel who brought revelation to the Prophet (s).

Down

1. The Qur'an was revealed on the night of _____.
3. The first five ayaat of this surah were the first ayaat to be revealed.
5. The first word to be revealed to the Prophet (s).

Divisions in the Qur'an

The Holy Qur'an is divided into smaller parts. The Qur'an was revealed in <u>ayaat</u>, (plural of ayat). These were arranged by the Prophet (s) together to form a <u>surah</u>. Later, Muslims divided the Qur'an into <u>Juz'</u> and <u>Manzil</u>. This was done to help those who wanted to complete reciting the Qur'an in a certain period of time. Join each of the four divisions below to its description.

AYAT	This is one-seventh of the Qur'an. Seven of these form the entire Qur'an. Any Muslim who wishes to recite the entire Qur'an in a week may do so by reciting one of these everyday.
SURAH	There are over 6,000 of these in the Qur'an. Some are very short, and others are long. The word means a sign, or a miracle. Each verse is a sign towards the right path, and a miracle of the Almighty.
JUZ'	This word is often translated as Chapter. There are 144 chapters in the Qur'an. All chapters are not the same size. Each chapter is made up of several Ayaat.
MANZIL	There are thirty of these in the Qur'an. They are all the same size. Any Muslim wishing to complete the reciting of Qur'an in one month may do so by reciting one of these everyday.

Stories from the Qur'an

The Qur'an tells us many stories. Stories of past Prophets, stories of good people, and stories of bad people. These stories are there for us to learn lessons from. The Qur'an itself says: *...therefore narrate the stories to them that they may think. (7:176)* Have you heard about the following stories? Read them and then answer the questions which follow.

Qarun

إِنَّا قَارُوْنَ كَانَ مِنْ قَوْمِ مُوْسى فَبَغَىٰ عَلَيْهِمْ وَاٰتَيْنٰهُ مِنَ الْكُنُوْزِ مَا إِنَّ مَفَاتِحَهُ لَتَنُوْءُ بِالْعُصْبَةِ أُولِي الْقُوَّةِ

Qarun was a man from the people of Musa. He rebelled against them. We had given him so much treasures that the keys of the stores of his treasures could hardly be carried by groups of strong men.

Al-Qasas, 28:76

Qarun was from the tribe of Prophet Musa. In the beginning he was a pious man. He accepted the belief in One God. But then he began working on a science which changes metals into gold. He became very wealthy and had many treasure houses of gold.

His wealth made Qarun very proud. Some people were jealous of Qarun's wealth. But others told him not to be so proud. "Don't be so happy with gold and silver which will pass away" they told him. "Do something which will please Allah and help you in the Hereafter. That is the world which will last forever, not this one." But Qarun would not listen. He became prouder and prouder.

Qarun began to insult Prophet Musa. He would not attend the gatherings where the Bani Israel prayed to Allah. When Prophet Musa talked to him, Qarun laughed and told his men to throw rubbish at the Prophet. Prophet Musa was very sad.

Allah became very angry at Qarun. He punished him by sinking all his treasures into the earth and causing him to die a terrible death. Qarun stepped onto mud which pulled him into the earth. People who were jealous of his wealth saw the miserable end of those who rebel against Allah. They were happy that had not been like Qarun.

Ashabe Qahf

اَمْ حَسِبْتَ اَنَّ اَصْحَابَ الْكَهْفِ وَ الرَّقِيْمِ
كَانُوْا مِنْ اٰيٰتِنَا عَجَبًا اِذْ اَوَى الْفِتْيَةُ اِلَى
الْكَهْفِ فَقَالُوْا رَبَّنَا اٰتِنَا مِنْ لَدُنْكَ
رَحْمَةً وَ هَيِّئْ لَنَا مِنْ اَمْرِنَا رَشَدًا

Don't you think the story of the people of the cave and the writing ar-Raqim was one of the marvellous miracles? When the youths sought refuge in the cave, they prayed, "Lord, grant us mercy, and help us to get out of this trouble in a right way.

Al-Kahf, 18:9-10

A long time ago, a King ruled over Rome. He forced people to worship him as their Lord. Many foolish people accpted that and performed Sajdah for him. In his empire lived six young people who were wise. They could think for themselves. They knew that the King could not be god. They decided to leave the country and go somewhere where they could worship the real God, Allah. On the way they met a shepherd and his dog who decided to join them. After eating from a nearby farm, they decided to rest in a cave. The group went to sleep, not knowing that they would sleep for more than three hundred years.

When they woke up, they looked at each other, wondering how long they had slept. One of them said they had slept for a day, while anothet thought it had been half a day. They were hungry and decided that one of them should go to town for some food.

When the man went to town, he was amazed at the way things had changed. Had he entered a wrong city? Everything seemed so different! He went to a baker's shop to buy some bread. When he gave his money, the baker looked at it in amazement. "Where did you get this from?" he asked. The young man replied that it was his own. The baker took the man to the King, saying that the man had probably found some old treasure as the coins were very old. The King asked for the truth, and the man told him the whole story.

The King then asked to be taken to the cave. The young man led him there and went into the cave. He told his friends what had happened. "We have been sleeping for a very long time" he told them. "There is another King now and he wants to see us." But the men were afraid that this King would arrest them. So they prayed that Allah would save them. Their prayer was granted and Allah put them all to sleep again.

2 **Test Yourself**

Answer the following questions
to find out if you have read
the stories carefully.

1. Each of the two stories teach us some important lessons. What did you learn from:

The people of the cave:_____

Qarun _____

2a. Allah always tests those who have faith. How are the people in these stories tested?

_____

_____

2b. Who failed the test? Why?_____

_____

3. Allah always listens to those who pray to him. How can you prove that from the stories you have read?

_____

_____

4. What adjectives would you use to describe the people in these stories. Write five adjectives for: Qarun _____

People of the cave _____

5. If Qarun had been a good man he could have succeeded in this world and in the Hereafter. On a separate sheet of paper write what Qarun could have done to please Allah.

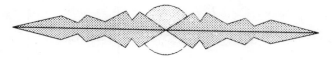

Teachings of the Qur'an

The Qur'an teaches us many things. It has rules to help us live a better life in this world, the dunya, and get a better place in the Hereafter, the Akhirah. Did you know that the Qur'an has teachings on things we do everyday like talking, eating, walking etc? Read the following ayaat of the Qur'an. Do you follow them in your daily life? Complete the sentence below the ayat.

Walking

And do not walk on the earth proudly, for you cannot cut through the earth nor can you reach the mountains in height. (17:37)

I must not
_____

Eating

. . . and eat and drink and do not waste, surely He does not love those who waste (7:31)

I must not
_____

Talking

. . and lower your voice, surely the most hateful of voices is the sound of the donkey. (31:19)

I must not
_____

Praying

Surely I am Allah, there is no god but I, therefore serve me and keep up prayer for my rememberance. (20:14)

I must pray to
_____

Now look up the following ayaat. On a separate sheet of paper write the translation of each verse and a sentence or two about it.

QUARRELING: (49:10))

BEHAVIOUR WITH PARENTS: (17:23-24)

TELLING LIES: (16:105)

REMEMBERING ALLAH: (2:152)

F U N

How many surahs beginning
with the letter A can you
make from these letters?
(Check your Qur'an for at least 5)
Write them on the lines.

_____
_____
_____
_____
_____

Each carriage of this train has a surah name on it. Join the correct wheels
to each carriage by finding out the surah number.

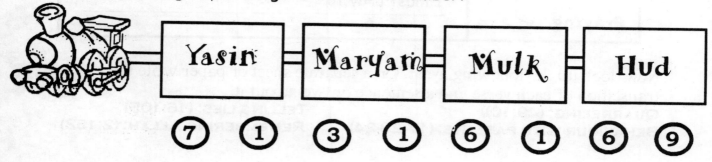

| Yasin | Maryam | Mulk | Hud |

7 1 3 1 6 1 6 9

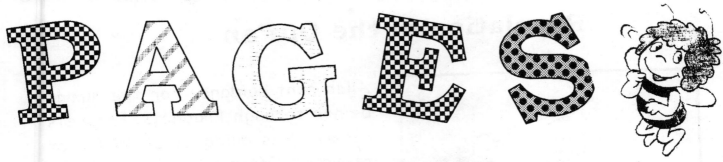

PAGES

Match the Surah names with their meanings

The Thunder	العنكبوت
The Spider	المؤمن
The Believer	القمر
The Moon	الرعد

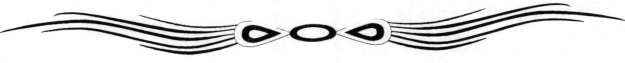

Answer these riddles!!!

(Clue: Look up Surah nos. 95, 44, and 105)

I am there wherever there is fire. I will cover the eyes and noses of those who have sinned. I am the name of a surah. Who am I?

_____

I am very big. I have very big feet. I have a very long nose. I am the name of a surah. Who am I?

_____

I am a fruit! I am brown in color. Allah takes an oath by me in the Qur'an. I am the name of a surah. Who am I?

_____

Revelation of the Qur'an

Allah sent guidance for the human beings through Prophets. Prophets receive this guidance by Wahy, or revelation. Often, revelation is brought by an angel. There can be other ways of revelation. Some Prophets like Prophet Ibrahim received Wahy through a dream, while some like Prophet Musa spoke to Allah.

The Holy Prophet(s) received Wahy through the angel Jibrail. The first revelation of the Holy Qur'an was on Laylatul Qadr (the night of power). It was during the month of Ramadhan. The Holy Prophet(s) often went to the cave of Mt. Hira in Makkah to think and meditate. He would sit there for a long time, thinking about the state of his people and how wrong it was to worship idols. On one such night, angel Jibrael came to him and revealed the first verses of the Qur'an. These were the first five verses of Sura Alaq, sura no. 96.

اِقْرَأْ بِسْمِ رَبِّكَ الَّذِي خَلَقَ

خَلَقَ الْأِنْسَانَ مِنْ عَلَقٍ

اِقْرَأْ وَ رَبُّكَ الْأَكْرَمُ الَّذِي عَلَّمَ بِالْقَلَمِ

عَلَّمَ الْأِنْسَانَ مَا لَمْ يَعْلَمْ

Read in the name of Your lord who created.
Created man from a clot.
Read, and your Lord is most honourable.
Who taught with the pen.
Taught man what he knew not.

(96:1-5)

Revelation of Qur'an

Allah
|
Jibrail
|
Holy Prophet (s)
|
People

Jibrael continued revealing the Holy Qur'an to the Prophet(s). It was revealed over a period of 23 years, in Makkah and Madinah. Sometimes the Prophet would be among the people when he received revelation. No-one would be able to see Jibrail except himself. At other times he would receive revelation when he was by himself.

Think and Answer

Color the circle beside the correct answer for each question.

1. The Arabic word for revelation is	O Hifdh O Wahy
2. **Revelation** often comes through the	O angel O human
3. The first **revelation** of Qur'an was in the month of	O Muharram O Ramadhan
4. The first word to be revealed was	O Fatiha O Iqraa
5. The Prophet (s) received the first **revelation** while he was in	O Mt. Hira O Quba
6. The first ayaat to be revealed tell us to	O read O play
7. Qur'an was revealed over a period of	O 6 years O 23 years

Qur'an Written Down

Whenever the verses of Qur'an were revealed to the Prophet (s), he recited them to his companions. He would tell some of them to write the verses down. The verses were written on various materials such as scraps of leather, palm leaves and other such items used for writing during those days.

Those who wrote the Qur'an were called scribes. While in Madinah the Prophet (s) had many scribes. A famous scribe was Zaid bin Thabit who was often called by the Prophet (s) to write down the verses just revealed to him. Zaid would bring his board, his ink-pot and his pen which was actually a bone, and then write down the verses.

The Prophet (s) told the Muslims how the verses were to be arranged into particular surahs. The proper arrangement of the surahs, and order of the verses were done during the lifetime of the Holy Prophet (s). After his death, all these written materials were compiled into one book, the Holy Qur'an.

There are many stories of how people converted to Islam after reading some verses which had been written down. When the people of Madinah first came to Makkah to learn about Islam, they were given written copies of the surahs that had been revealed. This shows that the Qur'an was written during the life of the Prophet (s).

Write TRUE or FALSE beside each of the sentences below.

1. The Prophet (s) wrote down the Qur'an himself. _____

2. The Qur'an was written down after the death of the Prophet (s).
   _____

3. Scribes wrote down the verses of Qur'an. _____

4. Zaid bin Thabit was one of those who wrote the Qur'an.
   _____

5. Muslims arranged the verses into surahs according to what they thought was right. _____

6. The scribes used a computer to write down the Qur'an.
   _____

7. The verses which were written during the time of the Prophet (s) were lost after his death. _____

8. The Qur'an was written during the time of the Prophet (s) but was collected and made into a book after his death. _____

Flying with Words

One night in Holy Ramadhan some Muslims set off on a hot air balloon. The balloon contained some familiar words. The following exercise will help you learn the words Replace each bold word with one from the balloon.(leave out words like the, a etc.). Then re-write the sentence in the space provided.

Laylatul Qadr
Jibrael
Mt. Hira
Surahs
Hifz
Qari

1. The Qur'an was revealed to the Holy Prophet (s) on a **special night.**

_____

_____

2. The Holy Prophet (s) was in the cave of the **mountain** when he received the first revelation.

_____

_____

3. The **angel** brought down revelation to the Holy Prophet (s) from Allah.

_____

4. The Holy Qur'an has 114 **Chapters**.

_____ _____

5. **Memorizing the surahs of Qur'an** is an act which pleases Allah.

_____

6. A **recitor of Qur'an** is one who reads it in the correct way, with a good voice and tone.

_____

_____

Surah Crossword

Across

3. Surah no. 104 of the Holy Qur'an.
4. An entire surah which talks about the Prophet whose brothers were jealous of him.
6. Surah 48. The name means Victory.
7. The surah which talks about prayers on Friday.

Down

1. The surah named after the mother of Prophet Isa(a).
2. The last surah of the Holy Qur'an.
5. The first surah of the Holy Qur'an.

Writing about the Qur'an

Write a few sentences about the Qur'an using the words below..

Book • • guides
teaches

recite • • Muslim
often

God • • message
Human being

The best among you is one who learns the Qur'an and teaches it to others

Longest Surah

Write the first letter of each picture to find out the name of the longest Surah in the Holy Qur'an. Then answer the questions below.

_ _ _ _ _ _ _

1. What is the number of this surah?

2. How many ayats does this surah have?

3. The last part of this surah contains the longest ayat in the Qur'an. Can you find this ayat? What is its number?

4. What does the name of this surah mean?

Shortest Surahs

There are three Surahs of the Holy Qur'an which have only three ayaat each. These are the shortest surahs of the Holy Qur'an. Do you know the names of these surahs? Write the first letter of the pictures below to get the names. Then answer the questions.

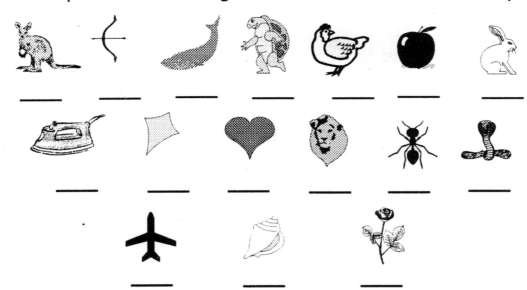

Write the name of each of the shortest surahs. Then write the meaning of the name, and the surah number beside it. Have you memorized these surahs?

1. _____

2. _____

3. _____

Hifz of the Qur'an

The Holy Qur'an is easy to understand and remember.
Allah says in the Qur'an:

وَلَقَدْ يَسَّرْنَا الْقُرْانَ لِلذِّكْرِ فَهَلْ مِنْ مُدَّكِرٍ

And We have indeed made Qur'an easy to understand and remember.

54:17

Many Muslims memorize the Qur'an, or part of the Qur'an. There is great reward for memorizing the surahs of Qur'an. The Holy Prophet(s) used to encourage his companions to memorize the Qur'an.

A person who has memorized the Qur'an is known as Hafiz of Qur'an.

How many surahs have you memorised? In the table below list the surahs of the Qur'an that you know.

Name of Surah	Name of Surah
1. _____	7. _____
2. _____	8. _____
3. _____	9. _____
4. _____	10. _____
5. _____	11. _____
6. _____	12. _____

How many more are you going to memorize? Make a plan to memorize a part of the Qur'an each year.

Surahs of the Holy Qur'an

Find the following ten names of Surahs of the Qur'an in the wordsearch below:

Baqarah, Yusuf, Nahl, Maryam, Yasin
Mulk, Balad, Ikhlas, Naas, Falaq

```
W  R  T  I  K  H  L  D
I  K  H  L  A  S  Y  K
N  N  F  J  L  Q  U  I
A  Y  A  S  I  N  S  J
H  B  L  A  H  A  U  M
L  E  A  N  S  S  F  U
B  A  Q  A  R  A  H  L
F  B  A  L  A  D  P  K
M  A  R  Y  A  M  S  T
```

Answers

Page 1
1. Qadir   2. Guide   3. Warns   4. Heals   5. Narrates

Page 2
Happy Face - Box 2   Sad faces - Boxes 1&3

Page 3
Suhuf - Ibrahim (a)   Zabur - Dawood (a)   Tawrat - Musa (a)   Injil - Isa (a)

Page 4
Huda - Guidance   Furqan - Distinction   Dhikr - Rememberance   Bayan - Narration

Page 5
Al-Qur'an al-Karim - The Noble Qur'an   Al-Qur'an al-Hakim - The Wise Qur'an
Al-Qur'an al-Majid - The Glorious Qur'an

Page 6
Mistakes: Qur'an not given to Prophet Ibrahim (a). Revealed in Makkah and Madinan. No changes. No other message to come. Nothing has been lost.

Page 8
Ibrahim, Yunus, Fatihah, Qalam, Hajj, Qasas.

Page 9
Wudhu, Shaytan, rush or go fast.

Page 10
Across: 2. Ramadhan 4. Hira 6. Jibrail   Down: 1.Qadr 3.Alaq   5. Iqra

Page 11
Ayat - Box 2   Surah - Box 3   Juz' - Box 4   Manzil - Box 1

Page 14
Possible answers:1.Faith, determination, courage, trust in Allah, not being proud, gratefulness.
2a) Loss of home and shelter, being away from family, fear, wealth (Qarun), fame.
2b) Qarun. He failed to thank Allah and help others.
3. Allah put the companions of the cave to sleep so they could escape the evil king.
4. Qarun: Proud, faithless, ungrateful, vain, greedy.
   People of the cave. Faithful, strong, brave, determined, intelligent, thoughtful.
5. Qarun could have been grateful to Allah, told people that it was just a gift from Allah,and tried to help the poor and needy.

Page15
I must not walk proudly on the earth. I must not waste. Imust not shout and scream. I must pray to remember and worship Allah.

Page 16
Surahs beginning with A - Anam, Aaraf Anfal, Alaq, Asr.
Yasin: 36 Maraym: 19 Mulk: 67 Hud: 11

Page 17
The Thuder-Ar-Ra'd The Spider-Al-Ankabut The Believer-Al-Mu'min The Moon-Al- Qamar
Riddles: Dukhan - Smoke (44)   Fil- Elephant (105)   Teen - Fig (95)

Page 19
1- wahy   2-angel   3-Ramadhan   4-Iqraa   5-Mt.Hira   6-read   7-23 years

Page 21
1- False   2-False   3-True   4-True   5-False   6- False   7-False   8- True

Page 22
1- Laylatul Qadr   2- Mt. Hira   3-Jibrail   4-Surahs   5-Hifz   6- Qari

Page 23
Across: 3- Humazah   4- Yusuf 6-Fath 7- Jumaah
Down: 1- Maryam   2- Naas   5- Fatiha

Page 26
Baqarah 1-Surah no.2   2-286   3- 282   4- The cow

Page 27
Kawthar - The Heavenly Fountain (108)   Ikhlas - The Unity (112)   Asr- The Time (103)

Goodword**kidz**
Helping you build a family of faith

Tell Me About THE PROPHET MUHAMMAD
What the Prophet's Message Is, Why His Life Is So Important and What He Teaches Me

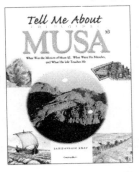

Tell Me About THE PROPHET MUSA
What Was the Mission of Musa, When Were His Miracles, and What His Life Teaches Me

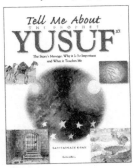

Tell Me About THE PROPHET YUSUF
The Story's Message, Why it is So Important and What it Teaches Me

The Prayer to the Merciful for Little Ones
Saniyasnain Khan
Illustrated by Bindia Thapar

Tell Me About THE HAJJ
What the Hajj Is, Why It's So Important and What It Teaches Me

Tell Me About CREATION
Scientific evidence demonstrates that all living things have been created by God
HARUN YAHYA

The Greatest Stories from the QURAN

THE STORY OF THE PROPHET YUSUF

Tell Me About Box
Goodword**kidz**

My Quran Stories Gift Box
Timeless Children's Stories from the Quran
Goodword**kidz**

Children's Stories from the Quran
COLORFUL WAYS TO LEARN ABOUT THE STORIES FROM THE QURAN

Quran Stories for Little Believers
I See Allah Everywhere

Quran Stories for Kids
"O YOU ANTS, RUN OFF HOME BEFORE SULAYMAN AND HIS ARMY TREAD ON YOU BY MISTAKE!"
SANIYASNAIN KHAN

I'm learning about... The Prophet Muhammad

Parent's Love and other Islamic Stories
Ishrat J Rumy

The Junior Encyclopaedia of Islam

PIZZA IN HIS POCKET
Learning to be Thankful to Allah
Astrolabe
Goodword**kidz**

I'm learning about... Eid-ul-Fitr

FUN TO COLOR AND LEARN Children's Stories from the QURAN
BIG COLORING BOOK-1

FUN TO COLOR AND LEARN Children's Stories from the QURAN
BIG COLORING BOOK-2

MY RAMADHAN FUN PACK ACTIVITY BOOK

FUN TO COLOR AND LEARN SEA ANIMALS In the Kingdom of Allah
DOT-TO-DOT, MAZE AND COLORING BOOK

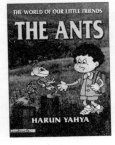

THE WORLD OF OUR LITTLE FRIENDS THE ANTS
HARUN YAHYA

HONEYBEES THAT BUILD PERFECT COMBS
HARUN YAHYA

BEAVERS SKILFUL DAM CONSTRUCTORS
HARUN YAHYA